TALES FROM THE
BALLET

TALES FROM THE BALLET

Adapted by *Louis Untermeyer*

Illustrated by *A. and M. Provensen*

GOLDEN PRESS ✦ NEW YORK

AUTHOR'S NOTE:

Ballets are stories with music but without words. The dancers express what is happening in pantomime, by movement and gesture. However, in telling these stories I have put words into the mouths of the characters. I have supplied speeches to go with their thoughts and actions. The words suggest what they would say if they could speak.

Notes on the origins of the various ballets can be found at the end of the book.

L.U.

Library of Congress Catalog Card Number: 68–21311

TALES FROM THE BALLET

Children's Matinée

PROGRAM

AUTHOR'S NOTE, 8

Overture, 10

OVERTURE

BALLET is a special kind of dancing—the word once meant "to spring," "to jump about," "to move the body in rhythm," in other words, to dance. But there is a great difference between dance and ballet. Unlike dance, ballet tells a story.

Ballet is hundreds of years old, some say thousands. It is claimed that it had its origins in ancient Rome, where a story was suggested by dancers who used pantomime and whose steps and gestures were accompanied by orchestral music. However, ballet as we know it today began in sixteenth-century Italy. It was not until then that it was enlarged into elaborate entertainments for the court of Catherine de Medici. Wed to the French king, Henry II, Catherine was so delighted with the performances that she introduced ballet into France. There the performers were members of the nobility; they were not only courtiers but kings. Several French monarchs played leading parts, and it was not until Louis XIV grew too heavy to twist and twirl that professional dancers were engaged, and the nobles became the audience.

From France ballet spread to Russia, where it had a great vogue, and to England where, in the eighteenth century, it was almost as popular as the masque, which was a kind of verse-drama, usually including dancing and singing. Much favored by the English aristocracy, the masque was formal yet lively, a forerunner of modern musical comedy. Most of the ballets at this time, like the masques, were based on mythological or allegorical subjects. There were variations, as in Milton's *Comus,* on the triumph of Good over Evil, and eighteenth-century spectators were wildly enthusiastic about a performer named Vestris, who danced out the legend of Jason and Medea.

For a long time ballet was earthbound—that is, the dancers rarely left the ground but slid over it in little steps with a kind of slow stateliness. There was small freedom to move rapidly and none to leap in the air until, in the early eighteenth century, a daring ballerina, Marie-Anne Camargo, shortened the traditional heavy skirts and exchanged shoes for heelless slippers. Dancing *sur les pointes* (toe-dancing) did not come in until the beginning of the nineteenth century when Marie Taglioni, the most famous dancer of the so-called Romantic period, showed how skillfully—and beautifully—it could be done.

Meanwhile, the choreographer, or dance-designer, had appeared. Jean Georges Noverre is credited with being the most notable figure in the history of ballet. Born in Paris in 1727, he danced at the court of Louis XV before he was sixteen, traveled to Germany, England, Italy, Portugal, and Austria, and was starred in practically every European capital. However, it was not as a dancer but as a dance-arranger that he was —and still is—celebrated. He freed ballet from its conventions, made it both more flexible and more dramatic by emphasizing the importance of the settings, using decorative backgrounds, brilliant coloring, and bold costumes. He created the "plots" of many ballets which went further than any ballets had ever gone in theatrical effectiveness. He invented new movements and had composers write original music for his productions—Mozart composed the score for Noverre's *Les Petits Riens* ("Little Trifles"). His books on the aesthetics of ballet and the techniques of the dance were standard works on the subject and were spread wide when they were translated into various languages. Before he died, Noverre's idea of a ballet made of many blended elements had spread throughout Europe. In France ballet became part of the opera as a *corps de ballet.* In Russia it retained its classical form, but many variants were added to the tradition, and ballet achieved new elegance and splendor.

The twentieth century brought about a new development in ballet. An American, Isadora Duncan, accomplished a one-woman revolution in the dance. Hers was scarcely dancing in the usual sense; she moved about in flowing rhythms on bare feet, clad only in a short tunic and filmy drapery. Her movements suggested an animation of Greek statues, a classicism intensified by the accompanying music of such classic composers as Gluck, Schubert, Chopin, and Beethoven. Isadora Duncan's innovations in dress and deportment were startling but, while she caused a sensation wherever she went, her departures from ballet were not taken seriously except in Russia. There her theories were incorporated in a new style of ballet and, under the leadership of choreographers like Michel Fokine and Serge Diaghilev, the methods of Isadora Duncan were combined with classic forms to perfect a "composite ballet" which could express anything—a simple lyrical idea as well as the most dramatic situation.

With changes in technique came changes not only in taste but also in subjects for ballets. For a while fairy tales were favored; stories like "Swan Lake," "The Sleeping Princess," and "Bluebeard" were greatly enjoyed. Then ballets began to reflect the backgrounds, the varied moods and activities of modern life. They recaptured the tempo and tension of the times, as well as the vigor and high spirits. Ballets based on folk themes like "Petrouchka," on frontier energy like "Rodeo," and on the modern scene like "Fancy Free" found hearty response.

Today's ballet presents a unique achievement—a fresh combination of music, drama, and painting: illuminating dance. It captivates the mind as well as the eye; it projects, in ever-changing pictures, quickly passing moments of beauty. Here is sheer magic: sculpture that comes alive, art in continual movement, embodied rhythm, a visual, pure, and wordless poetry.

THE WOOD NYMPHS

A GROUP of wood nymphs or sylphs *(Sylphides)* are dancing in a faraway forest. Sunbeams sliding through the trees light up the white flowers in their hair and their quivering silver wings. The sylphs drift to and fro as though wafted by a gentle breeze. Sometimes they seem like wind-blown leaves. Sometimes they move like white waves rolling in and retreating from the shore. Sometimes they are almost transparent, filmy figures seen in a mist.

Their dances tell no story, but they express heights and depths of emotion. The nymphs respond to the music in all its changing moods—sad in the Nocturne, wistful in the Waltz, gay in the Mazurka, joyful in the Grande Valse Brillante. Everything is radiance as the sylphs move exquisitely, ecstatically. It is like a beautiful dream remembered, like poetry realized without words and re-created in motion.

15

ONDINE

FISHERMEN and farmers are gathering in a Sicilian seacoast town for a two-day holiday. Today they celebrate the Festival of the Madonna; tomorrow they attend the wedding of Matteo and Giannina. Old friends greet each other; new friends are made. There is a lot of village gossip, a little drinking, and general dancing. Giannina is constantly kissed and congratulated; Matteo is continually patted on the back. Finally, the well-wishers depart, Giannina goes home, and Matteo is left alone.

He has work to do—he is a fisherman and he must get his daily catch of fish. He casts his net, and immediately it is full. After a considerable struggle, he pulls in, not the large fish he had hoped for, but a beautiful girl.

"Don't throw me back!" she cries.

For a moment Matteo is too astonished to speak. He stares incredulously at the lovely creature. Then he says, "What—who —are you?"

"I am Ondine. I am a water nymph. My mother is Hydrola, Queen of the Waters. And I am in love with you."

"But—but—you do not know me. You have never seen me before."

"Oh yes I have," says Ondine. "I have watched you often. You are the one I have chosen to be my mate."

"That cannot be," replies Matteo. "I am to be married tomorrow—to Giannina."

"That silly girl!' says Ondine scornfully. "Forget her. She cannot make you happy. I can. I can charm you with the sweetest

16

music your ears have ever heard, enchant your senses with delights they have never known, give you dreams you will never forget. I can show you the wonders of a world no human being has ever imagined. Come with me."

Matteo is tempted. But only for a moment. Other fishermen arrive; Ondine vanishes; and Matteo turns homeward.

His mother and Giannina have been waiting for him. He tells them what happened. Both women are skeptical.

"The excitement of the day has gone to your head," says his mother. "You must have nodded off and dreamed what you think you saw. Come, be sensible. Hold Giannina's skein of silk while she winds it."

There is a sudden breeze, the window flies open, and Ondine is in the room. She brushes the silk from Giannina's hand, smiles at Matteo, and darts to the window.

"You see," she calls to Matteo. "Your stupid Giannina cannot even wind a simple thread. She is not for you. You were meant for me, and I intend to have you."

With these words she dives into the sea. Water nymphs cluster around her, curious to hear for what reason she had left them. Ondine begins to tell them when her mother interrupts.

"My dear child," says Hydrola, "you are doing something that is not only foolish but dangerous. The land is not for sea-creatures, and the sea is not for humans. Earth-creatures are not like us. They cannot respond to the sensitive life under water. They grow old quickly and then they die; while we, who never age, live forever."

"I know that," replies Ondine, "but I would willingly become a mortal for Mat-

teo's sake. I would rather die with him than live without him."

"Patience, my child," says Hydrola. "Be sure of what you are doing before you make such a decision."

That evening the Festival of the Madonna is variously celebrated. First there is a wild Sicilian dance, the tarantella, so called because it is associated with the tarantula, a poisonous spider. It was believed that if anyone were bitten by a tarantula, a cure could be effected by whirling about rapidly, beating the earth, and banging a tambourine.

After the dancing, a church bell rings for vespers, and the people pray.

There is a fountain near the church and, before the praying is over, Ondine rises from it. She gazes intently at Matteo, and he grows confused. He crosses himself and looks at the Madonna. As he looks, the features of the Madonna change to those of the water nymph. He rubs his eyes and looks at Giannina. Her face, too, seems to be the face of Ondine.

"Am I dreaming again?" he says to himself. "Or have I been hypnotized?"

He is neither dreaming nor has he been hypnotized. Ondine has not only deceived him but has bewitched Giannina. She and her sister nymphs have lured Giannina into the water and Ondine has transformed herself into Giannina.

"Now," she says, running her hands over her body, "I am a mortal. It feels strange, for I am not yet used to this new form. And what is that at my feet? It is dark and changes its shape as I move. It follows me wherever I go."

She moves from left to right. Then she twists about, bends to the ground, and leaps in the air. But she cannot get away from her shadow.

"Alas," she says, "whatever it is, I must learn to live with it. Matteo will help me after we are married."

Putting on Giannina's cloak and hat, she walks slowly to her rival's home.

While Ondine sleeps in Giannina's bed, her mother Hydrola rises out of the sea and watches her anxiously. "If only I can make her see what I can see," she murmurs. The sound of the voice wakens Ondine and Hydrola disappears.

Ondine rises, but she feels weak. When Matteo calls for her, she has to lean on his arm. When he dances with her, she is so faint that she almost falls.

"Being a mortal is not so easy," she thinks. "I will have to practice."

Matteo is worried. Giannina always seemed so full of vitality, and now he is leading a feeble bride to the altar.

The wedding march begins and Matteo supports the substitute Giannina at the head of the bridal procession. Just as they reach the altar there is a noise of rushing winds and waters, and Hydrola appears with Giannina.

"I cannot permit you to ruin three lives," Hydrola says to Ondine. "You may be willing to give up immortality, but you will not be able to live as a frail human being. Moreover, you will be wrecking the lives of two mortals who need each other. Your place is with us. Come."

She takes her daughter's hand.

Slowly and with many a backward look, Ondine lets herself be led away by her mother. Sadly, she follows Hydrola to the shore and slips beneath the waves. As she sinks, a sighing sound is borne across the sands.

Matteo and Giannina join hands and the wedding goes on.

BILLY THE KID

His real name was William Bonney and, strange as it may seem, his birthplace was New York City. But he became the terror of the West as "Billy the Kid," a nickname that everyone feared. It was said that by the time he had reached twenty-one he had killed a man for each year of his life.

We see him first as a twelve-year-old boy in a frontier town. With his mother he watches cowboys gathering in front of a saloon while a few women from across the border do a Mexican dance called a *jarabe*. Some of the men have been drinking and a quarrel breaks out. The bickering grows into a brawl and, in the commotion, the Kid's mother is shot. As she falls, the Kid snatches a knife and stabs his mother's slayer. His days as a desperado have begun.

A few years later he is known throughout the land as "The Bad Man of Lincoln County." He defies the law, shoots his way out of every trap set for him, and, unlike Robin Hood who robbed the rich to give to the poor, he steals from everyone at the point of a gun.

His career does not last long. His downfall starts when he is caught cheating at cards by Pat Garrett, one of his pals.

"You shouldn't have done that, Billy," says Garrett.

"I do what I please," says the Kid. "That's my business. You'd better mind yours."

"There's such a thing as honor, Billy, even among thieves," says Garrett. "Friends have got to trust each other."

The Kid sneers. "Nobody's asking for your advice—or your trust. Or your friendship, either. You know what I do with people who don't agree with me, don't you?"

"I know," Garrett replies. "And I'm not staying for a demonstration."

Deeply troubled, Garrett rides away, joins the side of law and order, and becomes a sheriff. A little later he leads a posse to arrest the Kid.

The Kid has been expecting such a move; he and his outlaw gang start shooting. Blood is spilled on both sides; men are brutally killed; and, after a running battle, the Kid is captured and imprisoned. The surviving members of the posse celebrate their victory with a grim dance, a dance of death.

Before he can be brought to trial, the Kid manages a mysterious escape. He gets to the desert where he is concealed by friendly Mexicans and ranchers' rebellious daughters. He dreams of a girl with whom he would spend the rest of his life. In the dream he is no longer the tough killer with a gun; he is a tender lover as he holds his sweetheart in his arms.

He is still dreaming when he is awakened by the sound of galloping hooves. There are shadows all around him. They move closer.

"*Quien es?*" he shouts. "Who's there?"

A voice from the darkness answers, "Who do you think?"

"I always suspect an enemy," says the Kid, carelessly lighting a cigarette. "And who are you?"

"You shouldn't have lit that cigarette," says the voice. "It makes you an easy target. You want to know who I am? Well, I am your fate, your destined end. Goodbye, Billy." And Garrett pulls the trigger.

A crowd collects to view the body. Ranchers, lawbreakers, Mexicans, Indians, people of every kind and age. They place a Colt 45-calibre pistol at his right hand and, at his left, the knife with which Billy, while still a kid, had avenged his mother's death.

GRADUATION BALL

It is graduation time at the Finishing School for Young Ladies in Vienna. It is, in fact, the night before graduation, and everyone is tense. The young ladies are in a high state of excitement. So is the headmistress. The headmistress is particularly flustered, partly because she wants to show off her pupils at their very best, and partly because this evening the young ladies are to entertain a group of young gentlemen who are graduating from a nearby Military School. She runs from one pupil to another, giving last-minute advice, fussing with a headdress, tying a ribbon here, rearranging a ruffle there.

"Remember," she tells them nervously, "don't be nervous. Just behave naturally."

The young ladies try to act calmly. They smooth their dresses, point their toes, and rehearse the steps their instructress has taught them.

They are anxiously preparing when someone whispers, "They are coming!"

The cadets are prim young men. They have been so carefully trained that at first they seem almost *too* well disciplined.

Soon, however, they overcome their stiffness, and after their partners are presented, they waltz and whirl happily. One dance succeeds another—polkas, promenades, polonaises, mazurkas, quadrilles.

The dancers would like it to go on forever, or at least to last all night. But even the grandest Grand Ball must come to an end. The signal is given, and, alas, the merriment is over. Soldierly, with many a backward glance, the cadets march off, and sadly the girls go to their rooms. But many a romance has been started, and those who have come to know each other still dance together in their dreams.

THE FIREBIRD

THE MUSIC gives a hint of what is to come. It is mysterious, full of low murmurs and soft calls. It makes one think of unseen creatures whispering to each other, of strange birds in a strange country, of vague wings fluttering overhead, of stealthy feet creeping through an endless wood, of dark waters winding, and nameless things moving underground.

When light comes, it filters through a great network of leaves, for this is a forest. It seems to go on forever. There is no motion in the air, but the branches of one tree stir, heavy with many kinds of fruit. The mysterious fluttering grows greater. Then there is low thunder as a great golden bird flashes through the foliage. It is a bird that seems to be made of fire. Its feathers blaze

26

with crimson and orange; its eyes burn like fiery opals; its tail is a flaming comet.

Prince Ivan, out hunting, sees the bird. It looks like a great prize. He raises his bow, shoots an arrow—and misses. The bird flies away, but only as far as the upper branches of the tree. The prince hides in the bushes, and when the bird comes down again, he bursts from his ambush and catches the bird in his arms. The bird struggles, but the prince holds it tight. Then the bird speaks.

"Let me go," says the firebird. "Let me go, and I will give you something which will work wonders for you, something which may even save your life."

"What can you give me that has such power?" asks the prince.

"This," says the firebird, plucking a golden feather from its breast.

"It is indeed a beautiful thing," says the prince. "But how can it possibly do anything for me, let alone save my life? Still, it is a bargain. I will keep the feather, and you will keep your freedom."

With these words the bird flies off, and the prince is about to depart when a wave of melody sweeps through the forest. The music brings with it twelve lovely young maidens. They move in a solemn procession to the tree. There they are joined by an even lovelier maiden, a princess robed in white and gold. Together they shake the tree, catch the falling fruit, and throw pears, peaches, and apples of gold to each other.

It is such a charming picture that the prince cannot resist introducing himself. But the princess is alarmed.

"Do not stay," she warns him. "This is a dangerous place for a man, especially for

a man who might be a companion for us. Look!"

Following her pointing finger, the prince sees the walls of a large gray building not far away but almost hidden by the trees.

"That," she tells him, "is the castle of Kastchei."

"And who may this Kastchei be?" asks the prince.

"Haven't you heard?" she says. "He is an ogre, a monster, a—how can I describe him! Sometimes he seems to be part human and part animal. Mostly he assumes the form of a demon, one who will do terrible things to any man he finds on his property. And this is Kastchei's property."

"Nevertheless," says the prince, "I will stay."

The words have no sooner been spoken than there is a crashing sound. The girls run off; the trees shake; the earth quakes; and everything goes black. The prince tries to find a path through the darkness, but he can see no way out.

Suddenly there is a blaze of light and he is surrounded by a mob of devilish monsters, furies and fiends, a host of evil spirits. They seize the prince, who struggles to free himself.

There is another flash of light. The glare reveals a fearful demon. It is Kastchei.

"It is no use struggling," says the demon. "No one who enters my domain ever leaves it. When I cast my spell over you, you will become one of my captives, doing my bidding like these creatures here."

Kastchei raises a threatening hand—and at that moment the prince remembers the firebird's feather. He waves it. There is a rush of wings, and the firebird appears. Its

27

flame-like flight confuses Kastchei and dazzles the other demons. They release the prince, while Kastchei stands motionless.

"Now," says the firebird, "while Kastchei hesitates, you must act. At the base of the tree with the golden fruit, there is a hollow. Crawl into it, and bring out what you find."

The prince moves fast, and in a moment reappears with an iron box. Kastchei still stands transfixed, trembling.

"Open the lid," says the firebird, "and remove what is inside."

It is an enormous egg which the prince brings forth.

"This is the reason why Kastchei trembles with fear," says the firebird. "That egg contains Kastchei's spirit, the source of his magic. Break it, and you will break his power forever."

Kastchei springs toward the prince, trying to prevent destruction of the egg, but the prince hurls it to the ground. There is a terrifying cry as the egg smashes, and everything is in darkness again.

When the light comes back, it shines upon a scene of peace and beauty. Kastchei has vanished, his castle has disappeared, and his captives are no longer fiends and demons but handsome young men and lovely girls who have been under his spell. The beautiful princess, accompanied by her twelve handmaidens, comes forward. Court attendants follow her. They carry a crown and royal robes. All kneel.

"You are our deliverer," they cry. "You are our lord."

The prince smiles. "If I am to be your lord," he says, "this is my lady." And, drawing the princess to his side, he puts her hand in his.

THE SLEEPING
PRINCESS

It is a most important occasion that is to be celebrated this day at the court of King Florestan the Twenty-Fourth. The marble columns have been draped with magnificent brocades. The central staircase is crowded with noble guests. Guards resplendent in red and gold are stationed at all the doors. The thrones of the king and queen have been sumptuously redecorated with purple velvet and royal ermine. And in the most prominent position is that which makes this day most notable: a gold cradle. There is a high canopy over the cradle, and at the very top there is a gold crown, for it is the cradle of Princess Aurora, and this is the day of her christening.

Everyone is waiting for the function to begin. Besides the nobility, there are the Court Physician, nervously rubbing his white-gloved hands, and the pompous Master of Ceremonies, anxiously fingering a long parchment scroll. As he consults his scroll, he calls out the names and titles of the guests. With each name there is a drum-roll and trumpet call, the guests come forward and take the position assigned to them by the Master of Ceremonies. Finally when the king and queen mount their thrones, there is a longer fanfare, and the fairies troop in.

There are six of them, and each fairy brings a different gift and predicts a glowing future for the baby princess.

"She shall grow like a tree," says the Fairy of the Pine Woods, "and she shall be the most beautiful thing in the kingdom."

"Her complexion shall be the purest white and the softest red," says the Cherry Blossom Fairy.

31

"Wherever she goes she will perfume the place with the rarest fragrance," says the Carnation Fairy.

"She shall move more gracefully than the finest dancer," says the Hummingbird Fairy.

"Whatever she wears will outshine all things in splendor," says the Mountain-Ash Fairy.

"She shall have the sweetest voice that was ever heard," says the Fairy of the Songbirds. "She shall sing her way into every heart."

Each fairy then displays an appropriate present in a cage of gold, and the royal couple acknowledge each gift with delight.

"But," murmurs the king, "aren't we missing a fairy? Seven is the right number— seven days for the creation, seven days in the week, seven ages in the life of man, seven virtues, seven wonders of the world . . . There must be seven fairies."

As if in answer to his thought, there is a flurry of harp music and the Lilac Fairy floats in. She bows before the cradle.

"I have not forgotten you, little one," she says. "I am your fairy guardian, and I, too, have a gift. But that will come later. Meanwhile," she turns to the throne, "do not let me interrupt the proceedings. Let me join the festivities."

The other fairies pirouette about her, each one dancing in her own special way. Happiness is at its height when a blast of sound shakes the room. Thunder rolls through the sky and a whistling wind tears at the draperies. A black coach sweeps through a window. It has funeral plumes at the four corners and is drawn by four immense rats. The coach is followed by horrible looking creatures with long fangs and

hideous claws. The door of the coach opens and there emerges an ugly figure clad in a long black cloak with garish orange spots. She looks about her and grins wickedly.

"There is an *eighth* fairy," she says, leering at the king. "A fairy that you call the Bad Fairy because you are afraid she will spoil your fun. Let me see that list!"

She tears the scroll from the Master of Ceremonies.

"Just as I thought!" she says angrily. "I am not invited! Well, here I am! And I have brought my gift. Here it is!"

She, too, has a cage. It is of iron and it contains a rat. The rat squeaks horribly. Everyone shrinks from the sound.

"And now the prophecy!" says the Bad Fairy with a spiteful smile. "I cannot unsay what the other fairies have said. But I can add something. The child may grow up to be a sweet person, a graceful dancer, a lovely singer, and everything else, but she will not live long. One day she will prick her finger, and on that day she shall die."

Consternation falls on the court. No one can utter a syllable. Then in the shocked silence the Lilac Fairy speaks.

"It is now time for my gift," she says. "I, too, cannot unsay what has been said. But I have the power to soften it. The little princess someday may prick her finger, but she will not die. She will fall into a deep sleep, a sleep that *seems* like death, and the whole court will also fall asleep. She will sleep for a long time. But at the end of that time, she will be awakened by a kiss. And the one who kisses her will be a king's son."

Years pass. Princess Aurora is now a young lady as beautiful as the fairies had predicted, and there is to be a garden party to celebrate her sixteenth birthday.

The air vibrates with music and the ground throbs with the lively rhythms of dancing feet. The nobility mingle with the villagers to express the mood of this happy occasion. A group of girls perform a spinning dance until the Master of Ceremonies notices that they are carrying spindles and, horrified, he takes the dangerous distaffs away from them.

Four suitors enter. They are princes, and they have come from England, Italy, Spain, and India to win the hand of the lovely Aurora. She dances with each in turn, charmingly, courteously, but she does not fall in love with any of them. Her maids-of-honor add gaiety to the dancing, and soon everyone becomes a joyous part of the festivities.

Among those participating is an old woman. She is carrying something, and Aurora is curious.

"What may you be doing?" she asks.

"I am spinning," replies the woman, who is actually the Bad Fairy.

"Spinning? What is that?" inquires the princess. "Let me see if I can spin."

Because she is too anxious or careless, the moment she touches the spindle, the pin pricks her finger. She falls down, not dead but fast asleep. At the same moment everyone else sinks into a deep slumber.

The Lilac Fairy appears and waves her wand. Flowers shoot out of the earth, vines spread, trees tower, and a maze of foliage covers the palace, making an almost impenetrable labyrinth.

Again the years go by. Some say the princess lies sleeping for fifty years. Some say a hundred.

It is an autumn day when Prince Charming approaches the spot where a palace is hidden in the midst of a forest glade. The branches of huge plane trees and boughs of giant oaks intertwine to form a thick screen. The prince has been hunting; he, his tutor, and his retinue have been tired by the exciting sport. They decide to do something less strenuous—a game of blindman's buff. Everyone plays, even the tutor, who becomes the butt of the game. He is pushed about, catches hold of the prince, and makes so many mistakes that the others laugh and dance mockingly around him.

After a while the hunt is resumed. But the prince remains behind. He is moody, and a thought—or is it a dream?—passes through his mind. He tries to capture that thought, that vision, while the light fades. Then, like a far-off melody, he hears the ripple of a stream. At his feet a trickle grows into a pool, a pond, a lake. And across the water a boat made of mother-of-pearl with lavender sails draws slowly toward him. In it is the Lilac Fairy. She steps out and inquires why he is sad and alone.

"My life means nothing, because I am tired of doing nothing," he says. "The same court ceremonies, the endless talk, the stupid hunting. I long for something better. This place seems to have a kind of magic. I thought I had a vision of something beautiful. But it has gone."

"Perhaps I can help you to have that vision again," says the Lilac Fairy and waves her wand. Clouds descend, the trees are blotted out in mist, and through the haze Prince Charming sees the most beautiful of girls lying asleep on a golden couch. He falls to his knees in adoration. Fairies flit

about him as the sleeping princess rises— or seems to rise—and he runs forward. But she evades him, and though he pursues her, she is always out of his grasp.

"If I could only touch her!" he sighs.

"It is a vision," says the Lilac Fairy. "If you would see your desire as she really is, come with me."

Together they get into the boat. The mist grows heavier; the forest disappears; the boat glides down an invisible river. Then the clouds lift, and the Lilac Fairy points to a strange palace.

What makes it strange is that it is so still. Nothing moves; there is no sound of life. Guards sprawl in front of the gates; courtiers lie stretched out in chairs; a king and queen sit upright but motionless on their thrones. Then the prince sees the most wonderful sight of all: the sleeping princess,

even lovelier than she had appeared in the vision. Bending over her, he kisses her lips.

There is a burst of brilliant music, and everything leaps to life. The guards spring to their feet; the guests greet each other; the pages cavort with glee; the king and queen come down from their thrones. Then King Florestan places Princess Aurora's hand in the hand of Prince Charming.

"You have freed us from the spell of the Bad Fairy," says the king. "And if my daughter is still enchanted, it is with the enchantment of love."

"Yes," says the Lilac Fairy, "this also was predicted. Love makes everything live again—your hopes, your dreams, even the stories remembered from childhood. And now, for your amusement, I will bring your childhood and all its favorite fairy tales back to life. Observe!"

She waves her wand and the familiar story-book friends dance before their eyes. Here is Little Red Riding Hood accompanied by a playful wolf. Here are a couple of beloved cats: the clever Puss-in-Boots and the coquettish White Cat. Here are Bluebeard and Sister Anne humorously acting out the warning of the locked room. Here are the graceful Columbine and the agile Pierrot who, of course, excels in pirouettes. Here also are Scheherazade from the Arabian Nights, and a legendary Chinese Mandarin and acrobatic dancers out of Russian folklore.

All—human folk and fairy folk—join to celebrate the glorious event. All shower congratulations and kisses on the blissful Aurora. Never in her entire life has the sleeping princess been so radiantly wide awake.

PETROUCHKA

ON THIS day Admiralty Square in St. Petersburg is crowded to the last inch. Everyone is there in high spirits and holiday clothes, for it is three days before Lent, a time for fun and feasting before the long forty days of fasting. There is a carousel and a shooting gallery. There are side-shows and swings and booths full of sweets. There are toys and trophies and trinkets of every kind. There are loud-voiced "barkers" yelling at the crowd to walk up and buy. There is music—many kinds of music—a band, a barrel-organ, a calliope. And they are all playing (some of them out of tune) at the same time.

An organ-grinder is accompanied by a dancer. Another musician—this one carrying a concertina—has *his* dancer with him. And soon *everyone* is dancing, filling the square with life and laughter, with flying feet and flashing colors. Then two drummers appear.

Answering the summons, a queer-looking man enters from the center booth. He wears a beard, a tall hat, and a long robe embroidered with mysterious signs. He is the Showman and, as he waves his hands, the curtains fly back and reveal three puppets in three separate compartments. The people stare.

"You may well stare," says the Showman. "You think you are looking at dolls and, in a sense, that is what they are: a Moor, a Ballerina, and a Clown I call Petrouchka. But they are not ordinary dolls, and I am not an ordinary Showman. Watch, and you will see me give them the breath of life."

No one moves as the Showman draws a flute from his robe. He blows a few notes,

36

a fragment of a tune, and the wooden puppets stir. He plays again, and the three begin to move about, each in his own compartment. It is not long before they leave the booth and skip among the crowd. Petrouchka is the liveliest of the lot.

"You see!" cries the Showman. "I have put life into their veins and feeling into their hearts. Oh yes, they have hearts—hearts that can beat and break. But still," he adds with a peculiar smile, "they are only puppets. Nothing but dolls. Look!"

He waves his hands again, and the puppets collapse. They fall to the ground and the Showman puts them back into the booth.

But the life he had put into the puppets is still there. Their hearts continue to beat, most of all Petrouchka's heart, for he is in love with the beautiful Ballerina. He wants to stop being a clown and hopes somehow to win her. Next time he sees her, he leaps with joy, leaps higher and higher, leaps wonderfully again and again. But the Ballerina is not impressed.

38

"Save your strength," she says coldly. "Your antics are amusing, but nothing more. Remember, you are a clown."

Petrouchka is crushed. He hates himself. Still more he hates the Showman who gave him life and the power to love. The Showman's picture hangs on the wall, and Petrouchka hurls himself at it. He would like to smash the picture and break down the wall. But he only succeeds in tearing a hole in the pasteboard partition.

"Only a clown," he says bitterly.

While Petrouchka lies weeping, the Moor is idling, gorgeously clad, in a room next door. It is a luxurious room, decorated with Oriental silk tapestries showing green palm branches and fantastic fruits against a bright red background. The Moor is playing with a coconut. He tosses it about, then he tries to break it. When it does not break, he attacks it with his scimitar. Still it will not break. Believing that the coconut must have some sort of powerful spirit, the Moor proceeds to worship it.

While he is bowing to the coconut, the Ballerina enters coyly, playing a toy trumpet. Her playing and pirouetting delight the Moor, and the Ballerina lures him with smiles and sidelong glances. They dance together and he holds her close. At the end he pulls her onto his lap—and at this moment Petrouchka, hearing the music, smashes through the thin wall. Wild with jealousy he lunges at the Moor. Towering above him, the Moor laughs, and the cruel Ballerina echoes his laughter. Infuriated, scarcely knowing what he is doing, Petrouchka makes a frenzied attack. But the Moor brandishes his scimitar above Petrouchka's head, seizes him by the shoulder, and throws him out.

It is growing dark in the square, but the merrymaking is still going on. A flashy spendthrift, with a gypsy girl on each arm, scatters handfuls of money. A farmer entertains with a trained bear. Coachmen perform a Russian dance by themselves. Nursemaids dance with each other. Then nursemaids and coachmen dance together. Masqueraders disguised as devils, goats, and pigs whirl through the crowd. Rockets spill stars across the sky.

Happiness is at its height when terrible sounds are heard coming from the puppets' booth.

There is a piercing cry, and Petrouchka runs into the square pursued by the Moor, followed by a frightened Ballerina. He has not run more than a few steps before the Moor catches him and, with a sweep of the scimitar, strikes him down. The Moor and the Ballerina vanish. Horrified, the crowd surrounds the lifeless Petrouchka.

There are murmurs: "What a tragedy!" "It is a crime!" "Send for the police!" The muttering grows louder as the Showman strides into the center of the square.

"Good people," he says, "do not be alarmed. Look closely. This Petrouchka is not flesh and blood. It is only a puppet, a playtoy, something made of wood and rags, stuffed with straw."

Reassured, the crowd drifts away, and the Showman drags the limp doll behind him. Just as he reaches the booth there is a pitiful scream. Startled by the cry, the Showman looks up. And there, hovering above the roof, is Petrouchka's ghost pointing an accusing finger at him.

Terrified, the Showman drops the puppet and rushes away.

CHILDREN'S GAMES

A YOUNG girl, little more than a child, has been reading fairy tales and other stories in which animals talk and dolls behave like human beings. It is bedtime.

"How I wish *my* toys could come to life," she sighs. The book falls from her lap, her head nods, and her eyes close. Half asleep, she feels a soft breeze and hears a sweet sound as two figures glide into the room.

"We are the spirits of all toys," they whisper. "We are here to grant your wish."

"Oh," says the girl, "if only you could! I would give anything to see my toys move about by themselves!"

"Look, and you shall see," they smile. "We will begin with something unusual. Here is your top. Watch how beautifully it can spin by itself."

As the top begins to spin, the spirits touch the other toys. Soon the room whirls with fun and games. Two rackets play with balls and shuttlecocks, tossing and returning the most difficult throws all by themselves. A rocking horse neighs, rears, bucks, and prances on its hind legs. Dolls made up to look like Amazons battle merrily with each other, rattling their swords and clashing their shields. Soap bubbles turn into fairy-like creatures and float through the air. Men dolls become hunters, horsemen, and athletes. They race about the girl, begging her to dance with them.

Joyfully she dances with one after another. She dances and dances, breathlessly.

"Lovely! Lovely!" she exclaims. "It's like a beautiful dream!"

Alas, that is what it was. A new light comes into the room. It is the light of day, and with the dawn, the girl opens her eyes. There are her toys. They are where she had left them before she went to sleep—and they are just toys.

BLUEBEARD

Everybody loves the beautiful Ysaure, but she has eyes only for the humble Arthur, one of the least important persons in her father's court. He is a page, a young fellow with no hope of wealth or power. He and Ysaure have to meet secretly. Even when he serenades her, he has to wear a disguise. When Ysaure descends from the palace tower, her brothers, who have been watching, seize Arthur and unmask him.

"For shame, sister!" they chide her. "Consorting with a common page! You know we have suitably arranged for your future. Your husband-to-be is a man of property, and he is on his way here now. Prepare yourself."

Trumpets are heard announcing the arrival of a procession. The martial music grows louder as a large suite of retainers bring in their lord. He is a huge man and he carries himself pompously, aware of his importance. The brothers come forward to greet him. Ysaure holds back.

"But," she says in a frightened whisper, "he has a *blue* beard!"

"What's wrong with blue?" one of the brothers asks. "Blue is the color of aristocrats—blue blood."

"Besides," says the other, "you'll get used to it."

"But," persists Ysaure, "I hear he has been married before—several times."

"That shows he has had experience," says the older brother. "He will appreciate you all the more."

No time is wasted. Bluebeard and Ysaure are immediately betrothed. Bluebeard's attendants and Ysaure's handmaidens, joined by men and women as well as children from the village, dance about them. Then, with Ysaure's sister Anne as bridesmaid, they are married.

Arriving at Bluebeard's castle, Ysaure is amazed at its extent and magnificence. There seem to be hundreds of rooms. Her head spins as she looks in the mirror and thinks that she is mistress of this enormous establishment. She is not aware that Bluebeard has entered her chamber until he speaks.

"I regret that I must interrupt the honeymoon," he says. "But an impudent knight has dared to question me, and I must accept the challenge. I will be gone only a few days. Meanwhile, here are the keys to the rooms and the treasures. You can explore all of them, including the chests of gold and silverware and the caskets of jewels. But there is one room which you are not to open. It is a little room with nothing worthwhile in it, but it must remain closed. Here is its key. And remember, it *must* remain closed."

Martial music is again heard. Bluebeard kisses her on the forehead and marches off.

Ysaure cannot wait to examine the treasures. As soon as Bluebeard goes, she tries the keys. Room after room is opened and gone through; store-rooms, hall-rooms, ballrooms, bedrooms, reception rooms, dining rooms, each one richer than the others. Everything glows, dazzles, and quivers with light. Candles light themselves as she opens the doors. Sculptures come to life. Gold vases and silver pitchers move about and make bell-like music as they touch. Clothes-closets yield dresses from every corner of the world—India, China, Japan, Africa, South Sea islands—and the precious silks and satins weave about performing foreign dances. Jewels—rubies, sapphires, emeralds, diamonds—flash and flicker, turning the light into a kaleidoscope of whirling colors.

"Wonderful! Wonderful!" gasps Ysaure with each new revelation. "How lucky I am to have seen this all, and to have this all."

"Not quite all," something whispers. It is the Spirit of Curiosity. "There is one room you haven't opened. The key is still in your hand."

"I wouldn't dare," says Ysaure. "He warned me against it. Still . . ."

"Still," continues the Spirit of Curiosity, "it is as much your home as it is his. You have every right to find out what may be hidden. Even if you disobey him, what can happen? Surely you can take a look—just a *look*."

Taking a deep breath Ysaure unlocks the forbidden door. At first she sees nothing. It is pitch black. When she realizes that the shutters are closed, she opens them—and the daylight shows her a horrifying sight. Blood is all over the floor. And hanging from the wall are several bodies of women with their throats cut. Ysaure faints, and the key falls from her hand.

Hours later her sister Anne, who has come to visit, finds her there. Ysaure can hardly speak but, pointing, she gasps, "Bluebeard! His wives!"

"It was always said they had disappeared mysteriously," says Anne. "But this is no mystery. This is murder."

"Let us get out of here at once," whispers the terrified Ysaure. Then, picking up the key, she says, "Look! It is covered with blood!"

"We will wash the blood away," says Anne.

But the stain cannot be removed. Soap and water are not enough. Neither are pumice nor stone nor anything else they use. Frantically they scrub and scour, but the key remains red.

Once more the trumpets cry out, telling that Bluebeard is returning.

"Quick!" says Ysaure to Anne. "Get word to my brothers. Wave your scarf for a signal. Find someone who can take a message."

Anne runs out to find a messenger. Then she ascends the steps to the tower.

Bluebeard enters. "You seem disturbed," he says coldly. "You did not expect me quite so soon? Well, now that I am back, give me a kiss. And you might also give me the keys."

Ysaure kisses him nervously and hands over the keys.

"Thank you, my dear," says Bluebeard. "But there seems to be a key missing."

"Oh, is there? Perhaps I left it in my room. I'll see."

When she brings the key, Bluebeard eyes it carefully.

"How does it happen, my dear, that there is blood all over it?"

Ysaure turns pale. She has difficulty pronouncing the word. "Blood?" she stammers. "I have no idea."

"You have no idea?" repeats Bluebeard mockingly. "Well, *I* have an idea. I have an idea that you made up your mind to disobey my instructions. You unlocked the forbidden room. And what did you find? You found women who had disobeyed me once—but only once."

"Forgive me," cries Ysaure. "It will never happen again."

"You are right," he says. "It will never happen again. I warned you. Bluebeard never warns twice. And he never forgives. I will give you a few minutes to say your prayers."

Ysaure goes toward the tower steps and kneels. Then she calls to her sister.

"Sister Anne, sister Anne, do you see anything coming?"

46

"I see a cloud of dust," replies Anne, "it seems to be moving. That is all."

Ysaure continues to pray. Then she calls again.

"Sister Anne, sister Anne, do you see anything now?"

"The cloud of dust is nearer. Things are moving inside of it."

"Sister Anne, sister Anne," cries Ysaure. "Look closer. Are there horsemen in the dust?"

"Alas, no. It is only a flock of sheep. But wait! There is another cloud of dust moving more rapidly—and I can see horses now."

"For God's sake, wave to them! Cry out! Tell them—!"

Bluebeard interrupts her. "Enough! It is time for you to die."

"One more minute," begs Ysaure. "Only one."

"Not another instant," roars Bluebeard, drawing his sword. He raises his arm to deliver the blow. But it does not fall. Ysaure's two brothers rush in. One of them strikes down the weapon; the other runs his sword through Bluebeard's body.

"One more moment and you would have been too late to save me," says Ysaure.

"Here is the one who really saved you," says one of the brothers as the other brings in Arthur, the page. "It was Arthur who saw Anne's signal and it was he who brought the message. He deserves whatever you can give."

"I could give him this castle," says Ysaure. "But I do not care to stay in it another hour, and I do not think that Arthur would care to live here without me. Still, I can give him a little something. If you, my brothers, will consent, I will give him my hand."

It is Prince Siegfried's coming-of-age party, and his birthday is being celebrated with great gaiety. Siegfried is in high spirits; he dances with all the country folk. Everyone is merry, even Wolfgang, the prince's tutor who has had a little too much wine and attempts to show the others how to dance. When he clumsily trips, everyone is amused—everyone except Siegfried's mother, who enters with her court attendants. She frowns on the merrymaking.

"A prince! Dancing with peasants! You should have more pride!"

"Pleasure before pride, dear mother," says Siegfried. "We are all friends, dancing partners."

Her face is stern. "Partners indeed! Have you forgotten that tomorrow you are to choose a real partner—a partner for life? There will be no villagers at the ball. You will make your choice among court ladies."

The dancing stops. The prince's mother leaves, and young Siegfried's mood changes from gaiety to gloom. He had hoped to marry for love. His friends try to cheer him as a flight of swans passes overhead.

"Look!" they cry. "Swans! A good omen—and good hunting! The moon is up. Come along to the lake!" They take bows and arrows, and the prince joins them.

But he has little heart for hunting. When they reach the lake, he lingers behind while the others go off in search of game. He watches the moon go down and the dark night come on. The lake water murmurs softly; small ripples lisp against the shore. The hours pass. He nods, half asleep.

Suddenly the quiet of the lake is shattered; the ripples turn to waves, and a group of swans glides to the shore. If Siegfried was startled by the sight of the lovely birds, he cannot believe what he sees next. For, as a far-off church-bell strikes twelve, the beautiful swans change into the most beautiful of girls.

The loveliest of them wears a crown upon her head. Queen of the swans, she sees him and smiles.

47

"My name is Odette," she says, "and these are the ladies of my court. A wicked magician, Redbeard, turned all of us into swans. We are under his spell all day and most of the night. But his enchantment stops for a few hours at midnight. From midnight till dawn we can resume our true form and become human beings again."

"But will the spell never be broken?" asked Siegfried.

Odette blushes. "Only when someone of my own rank falls in love with me, someone—"

"Oh," whispers Siegfried, "I am already—"

"Wait," she says. "It must not only be someone who falls in love with me, but someone who is also willing to sacrifice himself, someone who is willing to die for me."

"Let me prove it," cries Siegfried.

Just as he tries to take her in his arms, the evil Redbeard appears and, disguised as a huge owl, savagely attacks him. Siegfried beats him off. His friends hear the noise and rush to his aid. In the dim light they mistake the girls for swans and are about to shoot arrows at them when Siegfried tells who they are. The enchanted girls are truly enchanted with the men and dance gaily not only about them but with them. The couples are exquisitely paired, Odette and Siegfried most of all.

There could not be happier moments for anyone. Odette knows she has met the love of her life. But she is as anxious as she is happy. Siegfried assures her that he is hers forever and that she has nothing to fear.

"Come tomorrow night," he tells her. "Come to the palace and I will declare you are the only one I will ever love. You shall be my bride. We will break the spell. I will be glad to live for you and die for you. I swear it here and now, and I will swear it again before the entire court."

Joyfully they dance, until the first faint light of dawn changes the girls into swans and they float away.

The next night the great palace ball begins. Everyone is wildly excited—everyone except Prince Siegfried. He sits listlessly on a throne next to his mother while guests from many countries parade and perform their national dances. His mother points out six young ladies of noble ancestry and hopes that Siegfried will choose one of them for his bride. But, though Siegfried courteously dances with them he can think only of Odette; he longs for her to appear. She promised to be there at midnight, and he cannot wait to present her to the court as his chosen bride.

Trumpets announce the arrival of two important guests and, disguised in the costume of a lordly black swan, Redbeard enters, accompanied by a ravishing creature. It is his daughter, Odile, but the magician has changed her to look exactly like Odette. Siegfried forgets that his beloved cannot come until midnight, when she resumes her human shape. His eyes deceive him and he rushes to Odile. Rapturously he dances with her again and again. He does not notice a white swan beating its wings against the window.

"I will never let you go," he whispers to the magician's daughter. She holds him close and prevents him from seeing the swan frantically trying to warn him.

"I love you only," he repeats to Odile. Then he turns to the court. "This," he announces, "is the daughter of the Knight of the Black Swan, and this is the one who is to be my wife. This, and no other!"

No sooner have the words been uttered than thunder crashes and a bolt of lightning sends the people scurrying for shelter. In that moment the swan gives a despairing cry and Redbeard and his daughter vanish. Midnight strikes, and Siegfried realizes what he has done. He has broken his vow to Odette. He has lost her forever. In a mad effort to find her, he runs out into the night.

He reaches the lake where first he saw Odette. It is now past midnight and she is there in her human form. But she refuses to look at him and hides among her swan-like companions. Finally, after Siegfried explains how he was tricked, she forgives him. But he cannot remedy his mistake. He has committed himself to wed another, and he cannot go back on his word. Odette weeps inconsolably, and Siegfried takes her in his arms.

Once more Redbeard works his wicked magic. He makes a storm lash the woods and causes the waters to rise, overflowing the shore. Siegfried carries Odette to safety, but the strain has been too much for her.

"I cannot live with you," she sobs. "And since I cannot be your wife, I will die."

"I will die, too," cries Siegfried. "Wherever you are I will be. Always we will be together."

Together they walk toward the lake. Sadly but serenely they enter it and the waters close over them. The spell is broken. A hint of dawn filters through the trees. The swan-girls, true maidens once more, know that Odette and Siegfried will never separate. In a vision they see the lovers meet the sunrise hand in hand.

PRINCE IGOR

PRINCE IGOR has been at war with his enemies, but his army has been defeated; he and his son Vladimir have been captured by the Polovtsians. The Polovtsians are a wild tribe, but their chief has a high sense of honor; he treats his captives with respect. Vladimir has fallen in love with the chief's daughter, and the chief has become friendly with the prince. To show his hospitality the chief arranges to display the native dances of his tribe.

"In the morning you will see us at our best," he tells Prince Igor.

Early next day the camp stirs to life. The Polovtsians are a fierce lot. They wear bold colors; their manners are crude; their faces are savage. But their hearts are good, and they are gentle with their women.

It is the women who begin the dances. One by one they emerge from dome-shaped tents made of dyed animal hides. A soft, slow music is heard and the women sway languidly to and fro, fluttering their filmy veils. Their bodies glide to the seductive rhythm. They sink gracefully to the ground, their faces half hidden behind their veils.

Suddenly the rhythm grows sharper, the melody wilder. Trumpets blare and drums throb as the Polovtsian chief springs into the center. He is a forceful figure, broad and tall, and his blood-red costume flashes like flame as he spins, whirls about, and leaps in the air. He flings his head back, strikes his bow against the earth, and shouts, "Victory! Victory!"

With a furious rush the warriors follow his example. They circle around him, surging left and right. Some of them kneel, some crouch, some raise themselves to their fullest height. All of them twang the strings of their bows as though they were shooting arrows against their foes. They imitate their chief, bounding in the air and leaping defiantly through space.

Then the women come forward. Again they glide voluptuously, waving their arms and holding out their hands appealingly. Instead of calming the warriors, their attitude excites the men into more frenzied activity. The women draw back as the rhythm grows tempestuous and the warriors stream forward in combat-like force. They pound

their feet; they shake their bows; they dash toward the women and carry them off.

Once more the music changes. This time it is delicate, a plucking of strings. Four young men step forward, tapping their toes and clapping their hands to the beat. Arm in arm they trip lightly, and invite the young girls to join them. First waltzing dreamily, then swinging madly, the youths and maidens sweep across the ground faster and even faster.

Now the chief leaps into their midst. His warriors follow him, and the thrilling climax nears. The dance becomes a riot, a rage, a storm of thudding feet and swirling bodies. Everyone stamps, everyone shouts, everyone echoes the chief's cry. They roar out the word, "Victory! Victory!"

The entertainment is over, and the Polovtsian chief offers his prisoner a place in his army. But Prince Igor will not admit he has been beaten.

"One day I will again head an army," he says. "And on that day I will return and defeat you."

"I admire your spirit," replies the chief. "Some day, perhaps, we will meet again on the field of battle. But until that day you are my guest."

However, the prince does not remain a guest much longer. Persuaded by his son Vladimir and helped by a Polovtsian solider, Prince Igor manages to escape. The warriors start in pursuit, but the chief stops them.

"Keep your temper and hold your horses," he tells them. "I would have done the same thing had I been in his place."

The story has a happy ending. Vladimir marries the chief's daughter. Prince Igor comes back to his country's capital and raises a new army. But he never sends it against the Polovtsians. When next he meets the Polovtsian chief, it is not as a military leader but as a friend.

Coppelia

THE SUN had just lit up a little town in Galicia when Swanilda came stealthily out of her house and walked across the square. She was in love with young Franz, and she came to have a close look at another girl who sat in the window of the toy-maker's house. The toy-maker's name was Coppelius and everyone said that the girl was his daughter, Coppelia. There was a mystery about Coppelia, for she never left her father's home. Yet, sitting at the window, reading a book, she attracted all the young men, especially Franz. Swanilda motioned to her, then called her name, but Coppelia never lifted her eyes from her book.

Swanilda would have lingered, but there were footsteps in the square, so she hid. Nevertheless, she saw Franz kissing his hand to Coppelia, and Coppelia seemed to reply. Franz had promised to marry Swanilda, but, even before their marriage, here he was, flirting with another! She ran out and reproached him.

"How can I believe what you tell me?" she said tearfully. "You swore to be faithful—and I find you making love to someone who smiles at every man who comes by."

"It doesn't mean a thing," said Franz. "I was just passing the time of day."

"Passing the time of day indeed!" said

54

Swanilda. "I won't listen to another word!"

Franz had no time to reply, for the burgomaster entered the square. He was followed by a large crowd that gathered to hear what he had to say.

"Friends," said the burgomaster, "I intended to read a proclamation. But I'll spare you the details. This is the gist of it. The lord of the manor is giving the town a new bell. It is to be hung tomorrow, and to celebrate the occasion there will be a festival. Moreover—and this is the big surprise—anyone who is married during the festival will receive an extra handsome dowry from the lord of the manor."

The crowd cheered, and there was eager conversation between many of the young men and women.

"And how about you, Swanilda?" inquired the burgomaster. "Haven't I heard that you Franz are ready to exchange wedding rings?"

"I'm not sure," said Swanilda. "I'll see what the corn has to say. Oh, it's just an old wives' tale, but they say if you hold a sheaf of corn to your ear, it will answer whatever you ask."

She passed a small sheaf of corn to Franz. "What does it say?" she asked.

"Not a thing," replied Franz. "Surely you don't believe—"

"I certainly do," pouted Swanilda, holding the sheaf to her ear. "It says something to *me*—it says you no longer love me."

Then, to show how little she cared, she turned away from Franz and led the others in a wild Hungarian dance. They danced until dusk when the square grew empty.

It was dark when Coppelius left his house, locked the door, and started off on his nightly visits. A group of youths came rollicking down the street and took hold of him.

"Come on, old fellow," said one of them. "Let's not wait until tomorrow. Let's start celebrating now. You're only young once!"

"Stop your mockery!" grumbled Coppelius. "If you don't let me alone, you'll have a taste of my cane!"

"Who's afraid of a cane!" they shouted, and pulled him into a wild dance. Coppelius teetered and tottered and finally got free of the pests. However, in the struggle he lost his temper and his balance. He also lost his key.

Swanilda found it. Coming along with her friends, she saw something lying in front of Coppelius' door. She recognized it for what it was.

"Now we can find out some of the secrets of this queer house," she said, putting the key in the lock. Then, to herself, "And I will find out what my rival who sits in the window is really like."

Just as they trooped in, Franz arrived with a ladder. He placed it against the window for he, too, wanted to see the lovely Coppelia more closely. Before he had a chance to mount, Coppelius returned, looking for his key, and Franz, fearing what might happen, ran off.

Meanwhile Swanilda and the girls were exploring Coppelius' rooms. When they came across his workshop they were startled, for they seemed to have entered a roomful of people. The girls screamed. All shuddered except Swanilda, who laughed.

"Don't be alarmed," she said. "Look! They're only dolls, life-size, clockwork dolls. That's all. Instead of being frightened, let's have some fun with them."

Reassured, the girls examined the mechanical figures and wound them up. Suddenly the large animated toys came to life —at least they became lively. A harlequin jumped to his feet. A bearded figure in Persian dress rapidly turned over pages in a book. A Moorish musician seated on a cushion struck his cymbals together. A Chinese mandarin played on a kind of harp. Then all began to dance.

While they were dancing, Swanilda searched for Coppelia. When she found her, hidden behind a curtain, Swanilda spoke.

"I want you to promise that you'll stop making eyes at my Franz. If you don't, you'll regret it. Do you hear?"

There was no reply. Swanilda became bolder. She seized Coppelia's wrist. Coppelia did not move. Her wrist was stiff; her arm was cold.

"Why," exclaimed Swanilda, "you're like the rest of them! You're just a doll! And *that's* what my Franz has been flirting with! I'll play a trick on *him!*"

Smiling, Swanilda removed Coppelia's clothes, put them on herself, tossed the pretty toy aside, and seated herself at the window.

The girls and the clockwork dolls were still dancing when Coppelius returned. He knew that someone must have found his key, for the door was open, and he could hear sounds coming from his workshop. He climbed the stairs as fast as his spindly legs could carry him. When they saw him the girls shrieked and dashed out of the house. The dolls' clockwork springs had given out, and the wooden figures fell to the floor. Muttering angrily, Coppelius set them

56

straight and started to see whether anything had happened to his Coppelia. He found her—or thought he found her—where he had placed her, behind the curtain.

"Ah, there you are, my masterpiece," he said, relieved. "Undamaged and lovely as ever. If any intruder ever dares to touch you, he will never touch anything again!"

A sound at the window made him turn. There, coming up the ladder, *was* an intruder, one he had chased away a little while ago. It was Franz. Coppelius was about to spring on him. Then he had another idea. He addressed Franz courteously.

"You have a curious way of paying a visit," he said. "But that does not matter. Welcome to my house. As a token of hospitality, let me offer you a glass of wine."

Franz hesitated. "Well, you see," he said, "it's hard to explain. I—well, I'm in love with one girl, yet I'm also in love—at least I think I am—with another."

"Don't bother to explain," said Coppelius. "Let's drink to your sweetheart—to both sweethearts."

Franz could not refuse. The wine was sweet. He did not know it was drugged.

"Another glass, my boy," said Coppelius. "Another glass or two, and you won't worry about which girl to choose. You won't worry about anything."

Once more Franz tried to explain, but he could not find the right words. His tongue was thick, his head was heavy. He fell asleep.

This was what Coppelius had been waiting for. He had always wanted to make a daring experiment—to draw life from a person and transfer it to a doll. Now was his chance.

"If I succeed," he whispered, consulting one of his books of magic, "I will have my heart's desire. Coppelia will live! She will truly be my daughter!"

He waved weird circles in the air; he uttered words in an unknown tongue; he made strange motions between the unconscious Franz and what he thought was Coppelia.

Swanilda watched all this without stirring. She understood, and she knew what she had to do. Slowly and woodenly, she moved her head. Then, stiffly, she lifted her arms, dropped her book, and, gradually, got to her feet. Still as expressionless as a doll, she moved across the floor.

Coppelius was delighted. "It worked! It worked!" he exclaimed. "My own creation! Coppelia lives! And she will do whatever I tell her!"

Swanilda smiled in obedience to his words. "Waltz, Coppelia!" said Coppelius. And Swanilda waltzed. "Now," he said, putting a tambourine in her hand, "do a Spanish dance." And Swanilda clicked her heels in a perfect fandango. "Next," said Coppelius, throwing a plaid shawl around her shoulders, "a Scottish jig." And Swanilda performed a Highland fling. "Now," he said, "do something of your own."

Coppelius was not prepared for what happened. Swanilda took him at his word. Swanilda took up a sword and made threatening gestures. She tore pages from the book of magic. She kicked the furniture about. She picked up the dolls and threw them in every direction.

Coppelius tried to stop her. "I have given her *too* much life," he thought regretfully—but Swanilda could not be stopped. She

went over to Franz and shook him till he woke. Half coaxing, half dragging, she got him to the window. Then she, too, vanished.

Coppelius did not know what had occurred. Searching for Coppelia, he finally found her on the floor, stripped of her clothes, motionless, once again a wooden doll. Rushing to the window he saw Swanilda in Coppelia's dress, crossing the square with Franz. Coppelius collapsed.

The next day was a sunny day for everybody. The new bell was blessed, and so were the couples about to be wed. Franz and Swanilda were the most joyful of all. The only jarring note came from Coppelius who forced his way through the crowd and demanded payment for what had been done to his workshop.

Swanilda was so happy at having Franz to herself that she felt sorry for the old inventor.

"Let me pay for the damage," she said. "It was my fault. He can have my wedding dowry to make up for it."

"No," said the lord of the manor, who had just distributed the wedding gifts. "Keep what has been given to you, Swanilda. As for the toy-maker, he has a just claim. Here, then, is a purse with enough money for him. Now let the festivities begin."

The bell was rung, and the square became the scene of a wonderful pageant. Players dressed to represent the hours were led by a figure representing Dawn who fled at the approach of Day. The bell rang again, and Cupid, the little god of love, appeared. The couples joined hands.

"That is as it should be," said the lord of the manor. "Be happy with each other not only all day long but all your lives. And so," he clapped his hands, "as the poet said, 'On with the dance! Let joy be unconfined!'"

GISELLE

It is a beautiful autumn day on the banks of the Rhine, a perfect day for harvesting the grapes to make the delicious wine of the country. The hills are purple with loaded grapevines that run through the fields to the very doorsteps of the peasants' cottages. Two of those cottages, thatched and half-covered with grape clusters, stand in the foreground. A castle shines in the distance.

A game-keeper, Hilarion, enters. He is in love with Giselle, and he suspects that she is being won away from him by a peasant called Loys. Loys stays part of the time in a cottage next to the one where Giselle lives with her mother. Hilarion has been watching Loys. Now he sees Loys coming out with a richly dressed servant. As the servant is dismissed, he bows deeply to Loys and retires. Hilarion feels there is something queer about such a splendidly dressed person bowing to a mere peasant. He does not know that Loys is really a nobleman, Albrecht, Duke of Silesia, and that he disguises himself in order to court Giselle. Giselle is a simple peasant girl, and it would be against all the rules if she were to be loved by any but another peasant.

When Albrecht (disguised as Loys) knocks at Giselle's door, she runs into his arms. But she is troubled; she has had a bad dream.

"I dreamed that you were being married," she says tearfully. "There was a large crowd. Your bride was not a peasant like me, but a titled lady dressed in silk and covered with jewels. You were yourself, yet not yourself. You wore a royal robe and carried a sword with a golden hilt—you seemed to be a prince. I was just one of the crowd, and I cried."

"Dry your tears," says Loys. "It was only a dream. It has nothing to do with us. Let us enjoy ourselves."

Enjoy themselves they do. Hilarion tries to stop them, but they ignore his gestures. They embrace each other and dance. They continue to dance with such light hearts and nimble feet that soon they are joined by others, by groups of grape-gatherers who put down their baskets and make the gay dance gayer. Suddenly a voice calls, "Stop!"

It is Giselle's mother. "Stop!" she repeats. "I am warning you! If you dance like that you will dance yourself into your grave. You will become one of the bewitched Wilis!"

"And what," asks Loys, "is a Wili?"

"The Wilis are girls," replies Giselle's mother, "or rather, *were* girls—who sang and danced and enjoyed themselves all too well, girls who were disappointed in love and died before their wedding day. Even in death they cannot rest peacefully. They still want to dance. Every midnight they rise from their graves in their bridal dresses. And woe to any man who meets them. They will surround him, they will embrace him, and they will make him dance until he drops dead."

The group shudders, but Loys laughs. "A tale to frighten children," he says. "Pay no attention to such old women's gossip. There's nothing to fear—and even if there were, we can dance fear away."

So they dance, merrier and wilder than before. They dance until they hear a hunting horn, the hooves of horses, and the barking of dogs. The interruption reminds the grape-gatherers that there is work to be done, and they leave. Afraid that someone in the hunting party might recognize him, Loys follows them, while Giselle and her mother go back to their dwelling.

Observing Loys' action, Hilarion grows more suspicious than ever. He decides to find out something that puzzles him, and slinks into Loys' cottage.

Meanwhile the hunting party arrives. At the head of it are the Prince of Courland and his daughter, Princess Bathilde. When they stop for a few moments' rest, Giselle and her mother bring out refreshments. Charmed by Giselle, Bathilde gives the girl a present and offers to find a place for her in the princess' household.

"Thank you, Your Highness," says Giselle. "But I am too simple for such service. I want only to serve my dear Loys, to dance with him and be loved by him."

"And who is this Loys?" asks the princess.

"My sweetheart, a peasant, but the handsomest and tenderest man in the world," replies Giselle. "He was here a moment ago; he should be back soon."

"I must see the handsomest and tenderest man in the world," smiles the princess. "We shall wait. My father is tired, and with your permission we might rest in your cottage."

"We would be honored," says Giselle's mother, bowing.

The Prince of Courland tells the hunters to go on without him and that they need not return unless they hear a horn.

After they have gone and the prince and his daughter have entered the cottage, the grape-gatherers reappear with their heavy baskets. Loys is with them and as soon as she hears his voice, Giselle rushes to meet him.

The others gather around the couple with cries of delight.

"Giselle must be Queen of the Grape Festival," they shout and crown her with a wreath of grape-leaves. "Let us dance together, all of us. Let us dance the Dance of the Vintage."

At the height of the gaiety Hilarion appears. There is triumph in his face.

"Look!" he calls. "Look what I found in Loys' cottage! Look at this velvet doublet and this embroidered mantle! Look at this sword with a golden hilt! These things do not belong to a peasant. I do not know who Loys really is, but—" and he turns to Loys, "you are not one of us!"

Mad with anger, Loys springs at Hilarion. Before he can strike a blow, Hilarion seizes the horn that hangs at Loys' belt and blows a loud blast. This summons not only the hunters but brings the Prince of Courland and his daughter Bathilde out of the cottage.

"Loys! Loys!" cries Giselle. "What have you done!"

"So this is the man you call Loys," says the princess. "Alas, my poor girl, you have been deceived. This is Albrecht, Duke of Silesia. He and I have been engaged ever since we were children. Our wedding day is not far off."

"Oh," sobs Giselle, "my dream! My dream is coming true! I cannot bear it!"

Her head swims, her knees tremble, her feet can hardly support her. She falls into a weird sort of dance, a mockery of the dance she had danced with her lover. Then, realizing that she will never dance with him again, she grasps Albrecht's golden sword and plunges it into her heart. She falls into the arms of her mother, who tries to restore her to life. But she cannot be saved. Giselle's spirit has gone to join the Wilis, those unhappy girls who, disappointed in love, died before their wedding day.

Sometime later, Hilarion and a few companions go out hunting. They come to a pool in the middle of a dark forest. Misty moonlight filters through the woods and makes the trees look like ghosts holding out long, leafy arms. There is thunder in the air and a flash of lightning reveals a marble cross at the foot of a cypress. The cross is half concealed by wild flowers; on it is carved a name: Giselle.

Dim shapes flit about Hilarion and his companions, fluttering forms like will-o'-the-wisps. It is a haunted place, and when a

bell in the distance strikes the midnight hour Hilarion and his hunters flee.

The ghostly forms turn into human figures, figures of young girls swaying in the moonlight. They are the unfortunate Wilis, and they are led by their queen. She waves a wand and the dancing stops.

"Tonight," she tells them, "we will be joined by a new sister. I will call her now."

As though wafted on a breath of air, the Queen of the Wilis drifts to Giselle's grave. Once again she waves her wand.

"Arise," she says, "and come to us."

Slowly the form of Giselle rises from the grave and bends before the queen.

"You are still weak, poor girl. But this will help you."

As she touches Giselle, a pair of wings spring from the girl's shoulders and a star shines on her forehead.

"Now," says the queen, "dance!"

And Giselle dances as though she had been restored to life and everything were as it should be. The others join her, and when, attracted by the dancing lights, Hilarion and the hunters return, the Wilis draw them into their midst. Circling about Hilarion, they turn faster and faster while he grows more and more exhausted. Dizzy, he is passed from hand to hand. Nearer and nearer the water they whirl until Hilarion stumbles, falls into the lake, and is drowned. His companions escape.

Albrecht, too, has seen lights in the forest. With his servant he enters the glade. As he approaches Giselle's grave, the servant urges him to depart.

"It is a strange place," he pleads, "and strange things have happened here."

But Albrecht refuses to listen. He dis-

misses the servant, and stands waiting for something, though he knows not what.

He does not have long to wait. In a moment he is surrounded by the Wilis and, among them, Albrecht recognizes Giselle. Knowing what his fate will be if she dances with him, Giselle motions toward the cross on her grave.

"If you hold fast to it," she whispers, "you will be safe. Nothing can harm you if you cling to the cross."

But the Queen of the Wilis overhears her.

"You are a Wili, and you are under my command," she says to Giselle. "I order you to entice your false lover away from your tomb. Make him dance to his doom."

Like her sister spirits, Giselle has to obey the queen. Her feet move against her will; her steps grow more and more alluring; her body sways seductively. Albrecht cannot resist her. He, too, seems to be under an enchantment. He leaves the cross, goes to Giselle, and embraces her. Encircled by the other Wilis, he dances with her. At first he dances delightedly, then desperately. His heart pounds; his strength begins to ebb. He feels he is dying, but he cannot stop. He is about to fall senseless to the ground when the clock in the church strikes four.

The striking of the clock saves him. It announces that dawn has come, and at dawn the Wilis must return to their graves.

Giselle is the last to go, and Albrecht tries to keep her from vanishing. But she cannot stay. She seems to dissolve in his arms. With a long sigh—or is it the dawn wind among the leaves?—she fades away. Her tomb opens, and Albrecht is left alone. His life has been saved, but he has lost his heart. Giselle has danced away with it.

RODEO

ORIGINALLY a rodeo was a roundup of cattle. Today, however, it refers to what can be done by the men who work with cattle—by expert horsemen, fancy riders, and lasso-throwers, men who love to exhibit their skills. A rodeo is a combination of excitement and fun, a daring contest and a thrilling entertainment.

Rodeo begins as the cowboys assemble. They come to show how cleverly they can rope cattle and brand them, how they can throw wild bulls and ride wild horses, how they can perform all sorts of difficult and even dangerous feats. Among the cowboys is the head wrangler who rounds up the livestock; a champion roper; and a cowgirl or two.

One particular cowgirl, dressed very mannishly, wants to prove she can ride and rope as well as any of the men. For a little while the men encourage her, but she seems to be awkward and they turn away. This annoys her, partly because she is ambitious, but chiefly because she wants to impress the head wrangler, with whom she is in love. She resolves to win his attention by doing something hard. She mounts a bucking bronco. The young horse has never been tamed and, though she tries desperately to stay on, the creature throws her off.

As she falls everybody laughs, even the girls from back east who are visiting the ranch—everybody except one sympathetic cowboy whom she doesn't notice. Her eyes are on the chief wrangler.

"If I could only make him look at me!" she sighs. But the head wrangler turns away and goes off with the ranch owner's daughter. The others follow after him, and the cowgirl, hurt and drooping with shame, is left alone.

That evening there is a big Saturday-night party at the ranch house. It begins with a square dance. Everything is lively and everyone is happy as the fiddles play and the square-dance caller shouts such calls as:

March around two by two;
Circle left and skip to my Lou.

Bow to the oyster, bow to the clam;
Bow to the partner with a grand salaam.

Lady 'round the lady and the gent also;
Lady 'round the gent, and the gent don't go.

Swing your partner, swing once more;
Promenade your partner off the floor.

Everyone is bouncing with delight—everyone except the cowgirl. The couples swirl by, but she has to stand by herself. Still in her mannish clothes, she watches the dancers enviously, and her heart almost breaks when she sees the head wrangler holding the ranch owner's daughter in a close embrace.

This is too much! She runs from the room with clenched hands and a determined expression on her face. In a few minutes she is back—but she does not look like the same girl. She has changed her outfit for a lovely dress; she has a ribbon in her hair and a necklace around her throat. She is by far the prettiest girl in the room.

Everyone stares. The cowboys throng around her; every one of them wants to be her partner. Even the head wrangler asks for a dance. She tosses her head and refuses all of them—all except the one cowboy who pitied her when she was thrown by the bronco and all the others laughed.

She smiles brightly as she dances off with the man of her choice.

THE GOLDEN COCKEREL

It ALL takes place in an imaginary kingdom where the most unlikely things are most likely to happen. In this wild country, witches ride around in iron kettles and small houses walk about on hen's legs. There is a queer light in the sky and all the colors are so loud that they have voices: reds scream, yellows clash their cymbals, blues blare like a whole choir of brasses. The flowers are ten times the size of flowers found anywhere else. The roses look like many-colored giant cauliflowers, and the daffodils have golden trumpets larger than the largest trombones. There is, of course, a castle. It is a mass of crooked turrets, leaning towers, lopsided arches, and crazy gates.

Suddenly an Astrologer, one who can see into the future, appears. He is an odd character, a magician who wears a high peaked hat shaped like an ice-cream cone, a long black gown covered with mysterious markings, and rings on every finger. He plays a few notes on a flute. Then he speaks.

"What you are about to see," he says in a thin sing-song, "may be true, and then again it may not. Some of you will laugh; some of you will cry. It may seem foolish, but there may be a lesson in it. It doesn't matter as long as you look and listen. And now let me present King Dodon."

A fussy, fat figure shuffles in. He hesitates, turns to the right as if to run off, turns to the left to see if there is any way to escape, and then comes cautiously forward. His velvet robe drags on the floor; one of his slippers has been lost; his crown slips over one ear. He is King Dodon.

In a cracked voice he calls his two sons. When they come, Dodon calls for his councillors. He can scarcely wait until they are assembled. He pouts, stamps his foot, and speaks like a bad-humored child.

"Why did it take you so long to get here?" complains King Dodon. "This is the fifth meeting we've had. And we've got nowhere. Well, why are you just standing there?" he says mumpishly. "Someone must make a decision. Are we going to wait for the enemy to attack us? Or are we going to make war against the enemy before he has a chance to attack? What is it to be? Well?"

"Well, Your Majesty," says one of the councillors, "I favor postponing action until spring. In spring the enemy will be busy plowing and planting. He will be unprepared for war."

"Hmmm," says King Dodon. "That sounds like a good idea."

"On the contrary," says a second councillor, "it is a very *bad* idea, if Your Majesty will pardon me for saying so. The enemy has many more soldiers in arms than we have. Besides, their troops have been highly trained in battle, whereas our army has been taking it easy during a time of peace. My advice is to do nothing."

"Hmmm," says King Dodon. "That makes sense."

"It *seems* to make sense," says a third councillor. "But, Your Majesty, it has not been given sufficient thought. We should first find out what the enemy intends to do. We should send spies into the enemy's territory."

"Hmmm," says King Dodon. "We certainly should find out something."

"Spies indeed!" a fourth councillor breaks in. "How do we know whether we will get the right information? We can't even speak the enemy's language. As for spies, how do we know that our enemy hasn't been ahead of us? There may be spies right here!"

"Here?" says King Dodon, bewildered, looking anxiously from one to another.

"Outrageous!" cries the first councillor. "What a thing to say! What does he know about the situation!"

"Ridiculous!" shouts the second councillor. "Instead of spies we should have secret weapons!"

"Absurd!" yells the third councillor. "There should be an organized campaign on all levels."

Then the sons join in. One is for peace; one is for war. The councillors continue arguing at the top of their voices. Each one tries to outshout the other. The quarreling grows worse. They jump to their feet and are about to strike each other when a voice even louder than theirs is heard.

"Quiet!" screams King Dodon. "Quiet!"

At that moment the Astrologer walks in. "I am bringing a gift," he says. "It is better than all your talk. I have brought King Dodon a golden cockerel, a magic young rooster. It is more than a pet, for it has marvelous powers. It can foresee trouble, and whenever there is danger, it can tell you what to do."

"Hmmm," says King Dodon. "A rooster who can talk! I can hardly believe it! Still, you are a magician, and it is only proper that you should have a magic bird, especially one who can tell me what to do. So," he yawns, "I won't have to do anything—at least not yet. Now," he yawns again, "I want to go to sleep. And," he says, addressing the councillors, "it would be a good thing if the rest of you went to sleep, too. All of you."

Obedient to the royal command, the two

sons, the councillors, and the entire court go to sleep. The only ones to stay awake are the ladies-in-waiting whose duty it is to circle around the king's bed, waving their scarves to chase flies away.

No one sleeps long, for suddenly the cock crows.

"Wake up! Wake up!" it cries. It has grown much bigger and its voice rings out. "The enemy is at hand!"

King Dodon wakes resentfully. Rubbing his eyes he mutters, "To arms! To arms! There's not a minute to be lost. To arms!"

But no one can find his arms. The captains shout, but they cannot locate the soldiers, and the soldiers cannot hear the captains. When they try to fall in line they fall all over themselves. The drums beat, the bugles blow, but the troops cannot even march properly. Bumping and stumbling, they finally stagger off.

King Dodon is still half asleep, but he makes a great effort to rouse himself. First he puts on his armor, but he cannot get it buckled. It crashes to the ground. After he manages to make it hang on, he tries to mount his horse. But he cannot find the stirrups, and when at last he gets one foot in place he cannot swing the other foot over the horse's back. Then his sword falls out of its scabbard, and as he bends over to pick up the sword, he drops his shield. His servants somehow get him on the horse and he clatters off while everyone cheers lustily. No one seems to notice that he has gone off in the wrong direction.

By the time King Dodon reaches the battlefield the battle is over. His troops have been beaten, his sons are lost, the enemy has disappeared.

"Alas," he weeps. "What is to become of my country. Worse, what is to become of poor King Dodon?"

His head sinks. As he lifts it, he sees a most peculiar thing. A large green tent rises slowly out of the earth. The tent flap is drawn back, and a beautiful woman emerges followed by a group of lovely girls.

"I am the Queen of Shemakhan," she says. "And these are my handmaidens. We have come to take away your troubles and gladden your heart. This is the way we do it in my country."

She begins to dance, her body swaying in the most languorous fashion. Her handmaidens imitate all her movements.

"You must dance, too," she says.

King Dodon consents. He is so fat that he can scarcely keep his balance. His feet get in each other's way; he stumbles, falls, and gets up again. He skips about like a drunken goat. The handmaidens titter. But he keeps on.

"Bravo," says the Queen of Shemakhan. "You have won my heart. I am yours, and I will go with you to your court."

"Hmmm," says King Dodon to himself, "the girls may have been making fun of me, but the queen realizes who I am and how to treat me."

A little later they enter the capital. As befits a king and queen, they ride in a chariot of gold at the head of a brilliant parade. The procession is composed of soldiers who had stayed at home, warriors who had escaped from battle, courtiers that had come out of hiding, and all manner of people out to enjoy themselves. Some of the crowd notice that while King Dodon carries himself like a victorious hero, the Queen of Shemakhan, who had only pretended to like the king, looks bored. As the procession ends, the Astrologer appears.

"Welcome home, Your Majesty," he says. "I have come to offer my congratulations and to claim my reward."

"Good," says King Dodon. "You are entitled to our thanks, and you deserve a reward. The golden cockerel lived up to your promise. What would you like for the reward? A bag of gold? A dozen slaves? A country home? A castle?"

"Thank you, Your Majesty. But I can have those things with the aid of a little magic. What I want is the Queen of Shemakhan."

"Impudent fellow!" cried King Dodon. "You must be mad! You shall have nothing! Not a thing! Out of my sight!"

"I do not want to threaten Your Majesty," says the Astrologer, "but I have ways to make you comply with my request. If you do not give me the Queen of Shemakhan, I will—"

"You will do nothing!" screams the king in a rage. "You will do nothing, for you will *be* nothing!" And with these words he strikes the Astrologer with his heavy scepter.

There is a burst of thunder as the Astrologer reels and a bolt of lightning smashes one of the steeples. The golden cockerel utters a terrible sound, flies straight at King Dodon, and knocks him down. The Queen of Shemakhan vanishes. There is a moment of intense blackness and grim silence.

Then the Astrologer reappears.

"As I told you," he says, "it is hard to tell the real from the unreal, the false from the true. Was there ever a King Dodon or a Queen of Shemakhan? Or even an Astrologer? Was it all a fairy tale? Or just a ridiculous dream? I leave it to you."

THE RITE OF SPRING

IN THE time before history was recorded, primitive man made animal and even human sacrifices to his gods. To insure fertile crops, men and women were often offered to the god of spring. This ballet vividly pictures such a ceremony.

The elders of the tribe have selected a young girl as their offering. She is the Chosen One. It is she who symbolizes the rebirth of the world, the return of warmth and light after the cold dark days of winter. She represents the spirit of regeneration, a power which she herself embodies but which must be extended to the whole tribe. A single life—hers—must be sacrificed for the life of the community.

Directed by the Old Man of the tribe, a group of prehistoric men, cave-dwellers and other primitive human beings, perform a rude ritual. They circle heavily around a fire; they stamp the ground; they utter hoarse cries in praise of the earth from which they sprang. It is not exactly a dance but a series of motions which suggest terror and triumph, birth and death, the basic and elemental forces of nature.

Then the Chosen One appears. There is a wild pathos in her movements, for she knows she is destined for a god and is, therefore, doomed. Bride to a bridegroom she will never be, she must dance until she dies. At first she moves slowly, almost fearfully. Then her steps grow quicker, her arms wave wildly, her feet fly faster. The rhythms are too violent to be sustained, but she dances frantically, hysterically. She dances herself into a delirium and, in a final spasm, death.

The sacrifice has been accomplished. The earth has been made ready. It welcomes spring.

THE PHANTOM
OF THE ROSE

THE curtains part and reveal a romantic
looking bedroom which a young girl enters.
She, too, is romantic, especially tonight, for
she has just come from a ball. There she has
met someone—perhaps *the* someone who will
be the romance of her life. She is not sure
of anything—she scarcely knows him—but she
has brought back a rose he gave her. She
looks at it tenderly. Then, with a sentimental
sigh, she raises it to her lips.

She drops the little wrap that covers her
white ball-dress and, happily tired, sinks
into a chair. Her arms rest in her lap, her
eyelids droop, the rose falls from her hands.
She sleeps.

A window opens and something blows in.
A youth—the living spirit of the rose—leaps
into the room and lands as lightly as a
petal. Wafted here and there by a zephyr,
he dances around her. She stirs in her sleep
and joins him. In the mazes of a dream,
they float in trance-like waltzes. Spellbound
they touch and tremble, and touch again.
Time seems to stop. They dance on and
on until . . .

Until the dream dissolves with the dawn,
and a breeze blows the youth from her
arms. The window closes.

She wakes and rubs her eyes. She looks
around the room. Then, with a secret smile,
she picks up the rose and presses it to her
heart.

THE NUTCRACKER

It is all merriment and make-believe as Christmas is being celebrated in the home of the mayor. He has invited the town's most prominent citizens, and he has also arranged a children's party for his daughter Clara and his son Franz. The Christmas tree has been trimmed, the presents are being opened, when a stranger arrives. He looks so queer in his odd clothes and with a black patch over one eye that the children are frightened until he speaks to them.

"My name is Doctor Drosselmeyer. It is, I know, a funny name. But I am a funny sort of man. I am a kind of Santa Claus, and the toys I bring sometimes—remember I said *sometimes*—do funny things. If you wind up these clockwork dolls they will dance almost—remember I said *almost*—as well as real dancers. Here is something for Franz. It looks like a pie but, as soon as you touch it, out pops a soldier ready to salute. And here, for Clara, is a cabbage. But it's a queer kind of cabbage, for in the middle of it is a puppet who can and perhaps—remember I said *perhaps*—will talk. That's not quite all. I have one more present made especially for a little girl. It is a nutcracker, but it's not an ordinary nutcracker. This nutcracker shaped like a little man was made by a magician, and he said—mind you, I said *he* said —it is a magic nutcracker. That's really all. And so good night, and Merry Christmas."

He shakes everyone's hand, and the grownups accompany him to the door.

All the children are delighted with the gifts except Franz. He sulks.

"I don't need another soldier," he grumbles. "I have plenty of soldiers. I want to see if the nutcracker can make magic. Clara, let me have it."

"But Doctor Drosselmeyer gave it to me. He said it was especially for little girls."

"I don't care what he said," says Franz, losing his temper. "I want it. And if I can't have it, you can't have it either!"

Clara tries to hold on to her gift, but Franz snatches it from her and throws it across the room. It lands on a couch.

"Let it stay there," says Franz, "for all the good it will do."

"Stop quarreling, children," the mayor tells them. "It's Christmas. Besides, it's time for the guests to go home and time for you to go to bed. Say good night."

Off to bed they go, but Clara cannot sleep. She cannot help wondering if the nutcracker really has magic powers. She tosses restlessly until midnight. Then she gets up and goes to the room where the toys have been left.

She cannot believe what she sees. The furniture is the same, but everything else is different. Everything is alive; everything is full of violent activity. Led by the nutcracker, the toy soldiers are waging a terrific battle against an army of mice under the command of their king. Clara cheers the nutcracker's regiment and, when it

seems that it is being defeated, she takes a weapon—her shoe—and hurls it at the king of the mice. The mouse army retreats and the nutcracker bows to her.

"You have saved me," he says, "and you will not regret it. Most of the time I am just a nutcracker, but tonight I am a prince.

Come, let me show you a magic kingdom."

Again Clara cannot believe what is happening. There stands a soldier-prince with a flashing uniform and a commanding form. Before she can utter a word, he takes her by the arm.

"I am going to show you the loveliest of

lands. It is called the Kingdom of Sweets, for in it you will find only the sweetest things to see, hear, taste, and touch. We must go through a cold country to get there, but do not fear. I have a sleigh ready. See, the snow has begun and snowflakes are dancing around us."

The sleigh-bells jingle, the horses neigh, and they are off. Over the frozen ground they glide. The Snow King and Snow Queen welcome them, and speed them on their way. Crystal-covered gnomes wave and caper until the flakes stop falling and the cold white earth turns green and gay.

"Welcome to the Kingdom of Sweets," says the sweetest of voices. "I am the Sugar-plum Fairy and I have arranged a festival in your honor. My attendants will bring you cakes and candies from every part of the world—and you will be able to eat all you want without ever getting ill. This throne is yours. While you rest here, dancers from all nations will entertain you. For every different flavor there is a different dance."

The Sugar-Plum Fairy claps her hands and the drums roll.

"Chocolate!" cries an announcer, and a group of Spanish dancers perform variations on tangos and fandangos.

"Coffee!" cries the announcer, and a troupe of Arabs exhibit their native measures.

"Tea!" cries the announcer, and a group of Chinese trip delicately in front of the throne.

There is a mingling of many strains of music, and Russian dancers leap in hopaks and trepaks. Flutes and reed-pipes play duets. Finally all sorts of flowers join in a grand waltz.

It is with the humming of a thousand instruments, the buzzing of innumerable bees, the dazzle of undreamed-of delights that Clara drifts from one beautiful moment to another . . . and continues to sleep . . . and to dream.

SCHEHERAZADE

KING SHAHRYAR should be a happy man. He is ruler of India and China, he owns a hundred magnificent palaces, and his harem has the most beautiful women in the world. His favorite wife, Zobeida, is seated with him upon a divan and she caresses him lovingly. But he is troubled. His brother, the Shah Zeman, has been deceived by his wife and puts an unpleasant idea in King Shahryar's mind.

"It's not that she's the only woman in the world," says the Shah Zeman. "I can get other wives, of course, plenty of them. But it would be the same story. I tell you no woman is to be trusted."

"How can you live without trust?" says King Shahryar. "If I didn't believe in my wives I wouldn't have a harem. I trust my Zobeida as I trust my brother. That's how sure I am."

"I hope you are right," says his brother. "I hope you will never find out how wrong you *may* be. You wouldn't like to put it to the test, would you?"

"Enough of that kind of talk," says King Shahryar. "Let us turn to pleasanter things."

He claps his hands, and a fat figure waddles in. It is the Chief Eunuch and he is in charge of the harem. He grovels on the ground and waits for orders.

"Music," says King Shahryar. "Music and mirth."

The Chief Eunuch strikes the floor with his staff and a group of odalisques, lovely dancing girls, come in. They wave perfumed scarves and make the room echo with the silver clashing of tiny cymbals held in their fingers and the tinkling of little bells on their feet.

King Shahryar watches for a while, but his thoughts are elsewhere. His brother continues to whisper to him, and he continues to shake his head. Finally he jumps to his feet.

"Very well," he says to his brother. "I will prove you are wrong."

He turns to Zobeida with a sigh. "I am restless," he says. "I must leave you for a few days."

"Has my lord tired of his Zobeida?" she inquires. "Does he seek comfort elsewhere?"

"It isn't comfort I seek, but activity. I have stayed indoors too long." Then to the Chief Eunuch, "See that my hounds and horses are ready. My brother and I are going to hunt."

Zobeida is downcast, but the other women show no sign of grief as the two men depart. As soon as they are out of sight, the women of the harem whisper to each other; they adorn themselves with jewels; they make their eyes darker and their lips redder. Then they bribe the Chief Eunuch. He opens two doors, and youths from foreign countries, handsome slaves, race into the forbidden harem. All dance wildly, all except Zobeida. She stands proudly apart, sad and a little sullen.

"He has left me for another," she says to herself. "He cares for me no longer. He has forgotten what he said. I, too, will forget." Then, turning to the Chief Eunuch, she says, "Open the third door. I command you."

The third door opens and a glittering figure darts through. He is in gold from head to foot, for he is a royal slave. He crouches before Zobeida, but she tells him to rise. For a moment both stand motionless, then she links her arms with his. The dancers form a ring around the pair and the circle revolves. Slowly at first, then swifter and swifter the figures move. Tambourines jingle, hand-drums are struck, and bells vibrate as the rhythm grows turbulent. It is an orgy of ever-increasing movement, music, and frenzied sounds.

Suddenly a still more violent sound is heard. King Shahryar and Shah Zeman crash in with a dozen armed men. The dancers shriek. Some stand panic-stricken; some cower and try to hide; some run to the doors which shut in their faces.

"You see?" says Shah Zeman. "What do you say now?"

King Shahryar is horrified. He shuts his eyes to blot out what he has been forced to see. Then, at the top of his voice, he shouts, "Slay them all!"

The slaughter is terrible. No one escapes. The royal slave is the first and Zobeida is the last to fall. After the uproar the silence is sickening.

King Shahryar bends over his favorite. "Alas," he groans, "what have I done!" He lowers his head and, weeping, kisses the closed lips of Zobeida.

87

FANCY FREE

THE PLACE is New York City on a hot summer night. Three sailors are on shore leave and, having nothing better to do, they are roaming the streets. Looking for adventure, they notice two girls who are without escorts. They approach the girls, who laughingly flirt with them. But there's a problem. There are three sailors and two girls, and the problem is which sailor is to be left without a partner.

"I've got an idea," says one of the sailors. "Let's stage a dance competition."

"I get it," says the second sailor. "We three think we're good dancers, and—"

"And," says the third, "the two best dancers get the two girls. Right?"

"Right," says the first. "I know a good bar and grill where there's a dance floor. We could have something to eat and drink first, if the girls are willing."

"We're willing—willing and eager," both girls agree. "It's a lovely idea."

The barroom is pleasant, the dance floor is wide, and the boys dance. Each one, in turn, shows off his particular style and character, and each one dances well. Sometimes the girls join them; sometimes they dance alone. At first the competition is friendly, then the rivalry becomes too keen for comfort.

When the girls cannot make up their minds and choose the two best, the sailors start quarreling. The quarrel grows heated, and soon there is a fight.

This is not what the girls came for, and while the boys are pummeling each other, the girls slip away.

Suddenly the sailors notice that the girls have gone.

"We're acting like idiots," says the first. "We're pals, three of a kind, aren't we? Let's stop this foolishness!"

In a minute they make up and swear never to get in an argument about a girl. They shake hands and all is well. Well, until . . .

Until they see a third girl—and it starts all over again.

THE Ballets

PRODUCTION NOTES

THE WOOD NYMPHS
Page 15

Whitest of white ballets, *Les Sylphides* is also the most popular. The choreography is by Michel Fokine who originated it in 1908. The music is by Chopin—in fact when the ballet was first performed it was called *Chopiniana.*

ONDINE
Page 16

Ondine (sometimes spelled *Undine,* from *unda,* a wave) is, as the name suggests, a water nymph. The libretto and the choreography are by Jules Perrot and Fanny Cerrito who, in 1843, danced the principal roles. The music is by the Italian-born Cesare Pugni who died in St. Petersburg, where the ballet was produced under the title *The Naiad and the Fisherman.*

BILLY THE KID
Page 20

The ballet of *Billy the Kid* is founded on the life of a real person and genuine events in the pioneering of the wild west. The choreography is by Eugene Loring. The music, which makes use of such authentic cowboy songs as "Old Paint," "The Old Chisholm Trail," and "The Dying Cowboy," is by Aaron Copland.

GRADUATION BALL
Page 24

Light, charming, and amusing, *Graduation Ball* is a fairly recent ballet. The choreography is by the Russian David Lichine, who was a leading dancer before he turned his attention to designing ballets. The music is by Johann Strauss who, because of "The Beautiful Blue Danube" and other famous compositions, became known as "The Waltz-King."

90

THE FIREBIRD   *Page 26*

The plot of *The Firebird* is derived from several Russian fairy tales about enchanters and magic spells. The theme of the ballet was worked out by the dancer Michel Fokine, and the music, later arranged as a symphonic suite, is by Igor Stravinsky.

THE SLEEPING PRINCESS   *Page 30*

The Sleeping Princess is founded on Charles Perrault's fairy tale which we know as "The Sleeping Beauty." Being a ballet, it is more elaborate than the story, and it brings in all sorts of characters not to be found in the original tale. The adaptation is by Marius Petipa. The scenery and costumes are by Léon Bakst. The music is by Tchaikovsky.

PETROUCHKA   *Page 36*

The story of *Petrouchka* originated with the Russian composer Igor Stravinsky, who wrote the music for it. He first suggested it to the producer Serge Diaghilev and then worked out folklore details with the painter-designer Alexandre Benois, who supplied the scenery and costumes. The choreography is by the Russian dancer Michel Fokine.

CHILDREN'S GAMES   *Page 41*

Children's Games (Jeux d'Enfants) is a ballet whose fantastic nature is emphasized in the scenery and costumes by the surrealist painter Joan Miró. The book is by the poet Boris Kochno. The choreography is by the dancer Leonide Massine. The music is by Georges Bizet who composed, among other famous works, *Carmen*.

BLUEBEARD   *Page 42*

The ballet of *Bluebeard* is a Russian version of Charles Perrault's grim fairy tale. The adaptation is by Lydia Pashkova. The choreography is by the dancer and dance director Marius Petipa. The music is by Peter Petrovich Schneck of St. Petersburg, where the ballet was first produced in 1896.

SWAN LAKE   *Page 47*

Swan Lake is one of the most famous of the "white ballets," so called because the dancers almost always wear white costumes. In its complete form it is a four-act ballet, but it is often performed in shorter versions.

The music is by Tchaikovsky, the plot by Begitchev and Geltser, the choreography by Petipa and Ivanov.

PRINCE IGOR   *Page 51*

The full title of this ballet should be *The Polovtsian Dances from Prince Igor. Prince Igor* is an opera by Alexandre Borodin, the Russian composer who was also a distinguished chemist. The dances in the second act are part of an entertainment for the prince by the Polovtsian warriors and their women. The original scenery and costumes were by the Russian painter Nicholas Roerich, and the choreography is by the Russian dancer Michel Fokine.

COPPELIA   *Page 54*

Coppelia, which has a subtitle, *The Girl with Enamel Eyes,* was first danced a hundred years ago by a fifteen-year-old girl, who lived to give only eighteen performances. The book and choreography are by Arthur Saint-Leon. The music is by the French composer Leo Delibes who wrote many graceful operatic and ballet scores.

GISELLE   *Page 61*

First performed as a ballet more than a century ago, the story of *Giselle* is founded on a Rhineland legend told by the German poet Heinrich Heine and adapted by the French poet, Théophile Gautier with Vernoy de Saint-Georges. The choreography is by Jean Coralli and the music by Adolphe Adam.

RODEO   *Page 67*

Rodeo is one of the most native American ballets. The story and choreography are by the American dancer and dance designer, Agnes de Mille. The music is by the American composer Aaron Copland. It was first performed at the Metropolitan Opera House in 1942.

THE GOLDEN COCKEREL   *Page 70*

The Golden Cockerel (Le Coq d'Or) is a comic fairy tale based on a poem by Alexandre Pushkin, Russia's greatest poet. It is a combination of opera and ballet, for in most productions singers tell what the dancers are expressing. The libretto is by Alexandre Benois. The choreography is by the dancer Michel Fokine. The music is by Nicolas Rimsky-Korsakov, a naval officer and a composer who chose national subjects and made brilliant variations of Russian folk-melodies.

THE RITE OF SPRING
Page 76

When *The Rite of Spring (Le Sacre du Printemps)* had its first performance in 1913 in Paris the audience reacted violently. The primitive subject and the strange, exciting music which accentuated it struck its hearers almost like physical blows. The audience struck back with groans, shouts, howls, whistles, and angry catcalls. Today *Le Sacre du Printemps* is a classic. The choreography is by the famous dancer Vaslav Nijinsky. Both the book and the music are by Igor Stravinsky.

THE PHANTOM OF THE ROSE
Page 78

The Phantom of the Rose (Le Spectre de la Rose) is, as the title indicates, a fantasy. It was suggested by a poem by Théophile Gautier and set to the music of Karl Maria von Weber's internationally famous "Invitation to the Dance." The choreography is by Michel Fokine. First performed in 1911, the ballet was a sensation with Nijinsky in the title role.

THE NUTCRACKER
Page 80

The story of *The Nutcracker* (or *Casse Noisette*) is borrowed from a tale called "The Nutcracker and the King of the Mice" by the versatile German writer E. T. A. Hoffmann. What plot there is is by L. I. Ivanov who also designed the choreography. The music, which has thrilled millions in its arrangement as a concert suite, is by Tchaikovsky. One of the most popular of ballets, *The Nutcracker* is a cornucopia of dancing delight.

SCHEHERAZADE
Page 85

The tales known as "The Arabian Nights" are supposed to have been told by Scheherazade to her lord, the Sultan. The Sultan's first wife had been unfaithful, and he had sworn to wed another woman every night and have her killed the next morning. Scheherazade saved her life by telling the Sultan a story on her wedding night but not finishing it. The Sultan was so eager to hear the end of it that he postponed her execution. So for one thousand and one nights Scheherazade continued to tell stories, and the Sultan was so delighted that he gave up his cruel plan. The first story in "The Arabian Nights" was made into a ballet by the painter Alexandre Benois. The choreography is by Michel Fokine, the original scenery and costumes were by Leon Bakst, and the music is taken from the famous symphonic suite by Rimsky-Korsakov.

FANCY FREE
Page 88

Fancy Free was first produced at the Metropolitan Opera House in 1944. It was such a success that it was made into an equally successful musical comedy called *On the Town*. The choreography is by Jerome Robbins, a dancer with the American Ballet Theatre who became a noted director. The music is by Leonard Bernstein, the famous composer and internationally known conductor.

CURTAIN